This edition published by Parragon in 2012
Parragon
Chartist House
15-17 Trim Street
Bath BA1 1HA, UK
www.parragon.com

ISBN 978-1-4454-8155-5
Printed in China

Beauty and the Beast

Adapted by Ellen Titlebaum

Bath · New York · Singapore · Hong Kong · Cologne · Delhi
Melbourne · Amsterdam · Johannesburg · Auckland · Shenzhen

Once upon a time, an old beggar woman appeared at a castle where there lived a prince. She offered the prince a single red rose in return for shelter. But he sneered at her gift and turned the old woman away.

"Do not be deceived by appearances," the beggar warned, and suddenly transformed into a beautiful enchantress! The prince begged forgiveness, but he was too late. The enchantress had seen there was no love in the heart of this selfish prince.

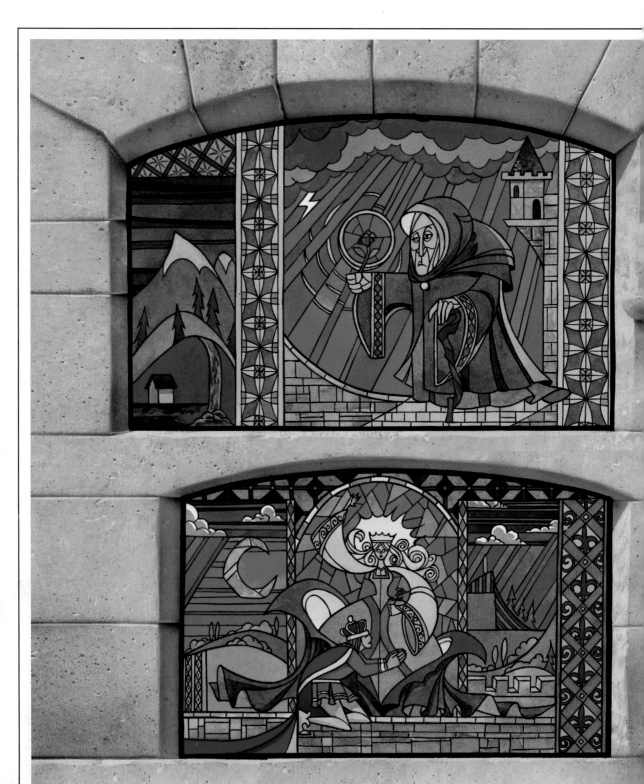

As a punishment, the enchantress turned the prince into a terrifying beast and cast a spell on everyone in the castle.

Giving the Beast a magic rose she said, "This will bloom until your twenty-first year. If you learn to love another and earn that person's love before the last petal falls, the spell will be broken. Otherwise, you will remain a Beast forever."

9

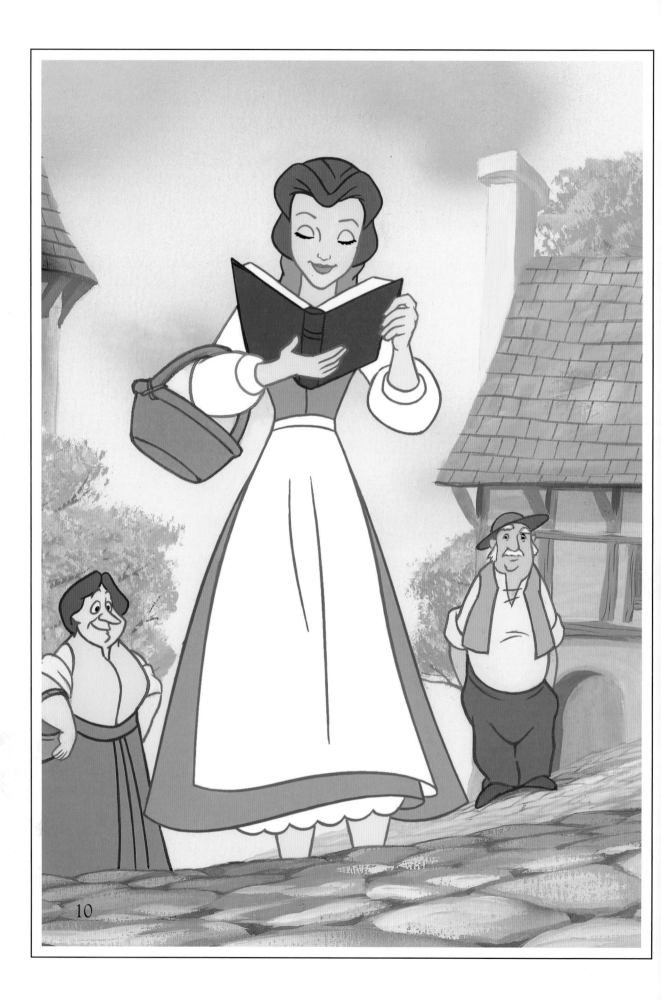

Belle lived in a village near the castle. She loved to read books about adventure and romance.

One morning, Gaston the hunter saw Belle and boasted, "That's the girl I'm going to marry."

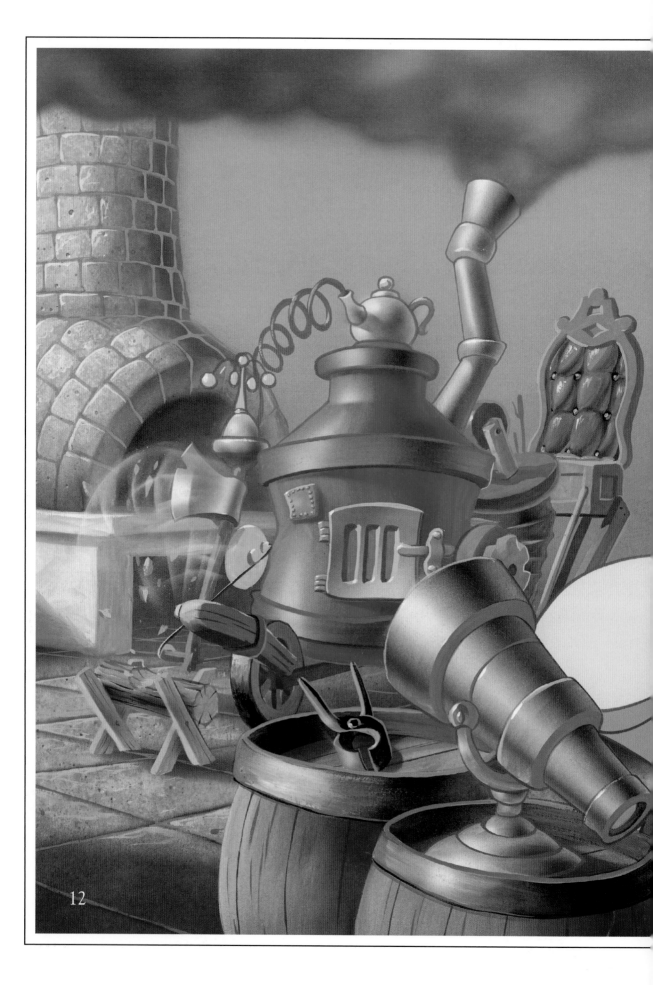

At Belle's house, her father, Maurice, was working on a new invention.

"You'll win first prize at the fair tomorrow," predicted Belle.

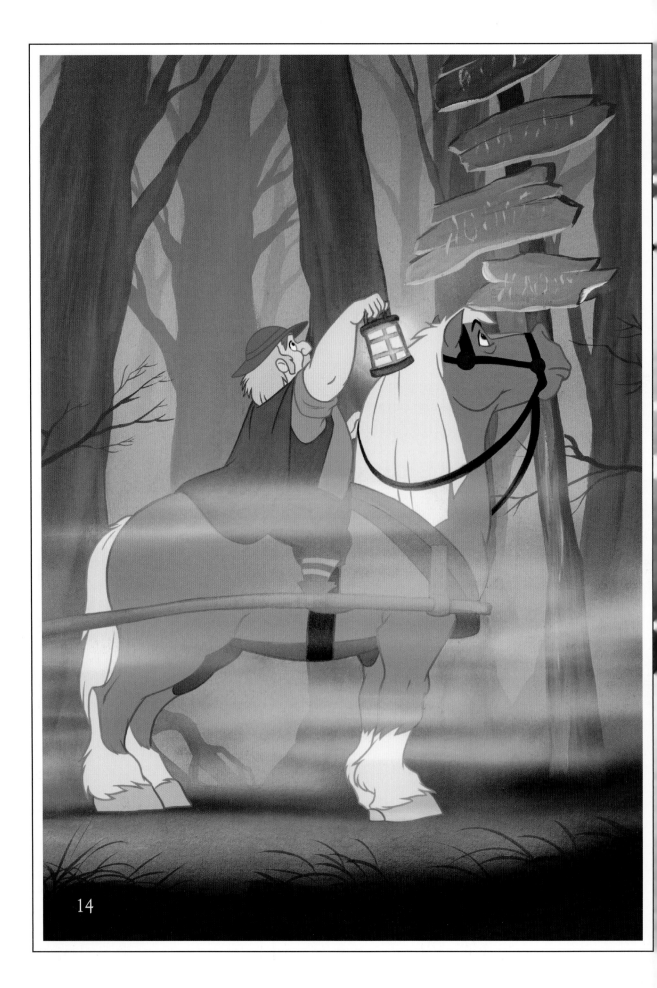

But Maurice and his horse Philippe never made it to the fair. They became lost in the dark forest.

Black bats flew out of the shadows, followed by growling wolves. The terrified horse threw his rider off and charged into the woods.

Maurice ran down a hillside, crashing into branches and toppling over gigantic roots until he saw an old gate in front of a castle.

He forced the gate open and escaped just before the wolves reached him!

16

Maurice approached the castle, and stepped inside. "Not a word," whispered Cogsworth, the clock, to Lumiere, the candelabrum. The people in the castle had been changed into enchanted objects!

Friendly Lumiere announced, "Welcome, Monsieur!"

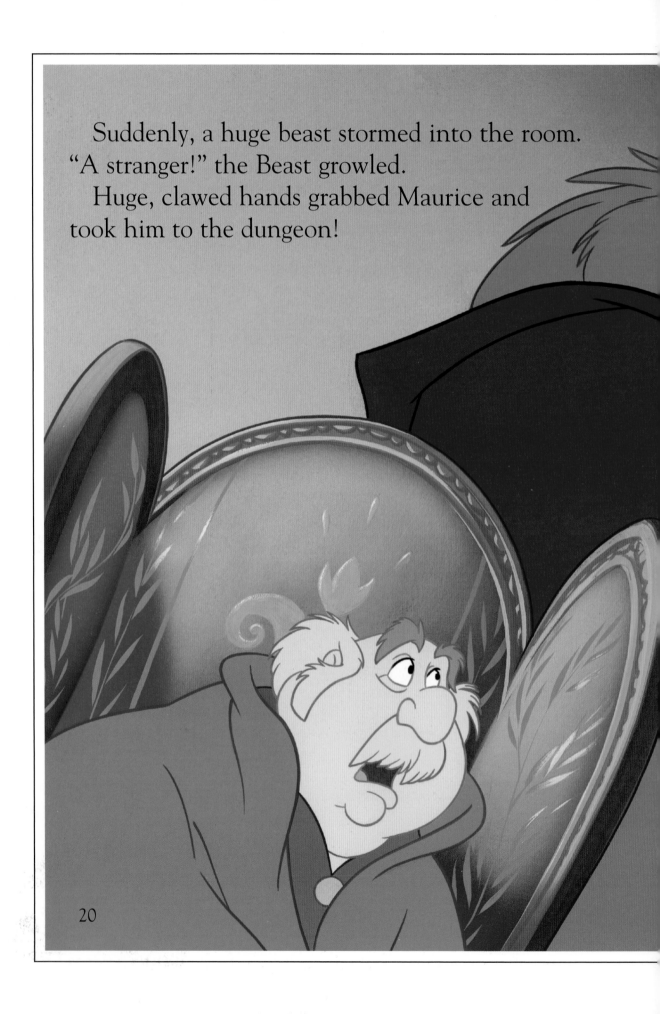

Suddenly, a huge beast stormed into the room.
"A stranger!" the Beast growled.
Huge, clawed hands grabbed Maurice and
took him to the dungeon!

20

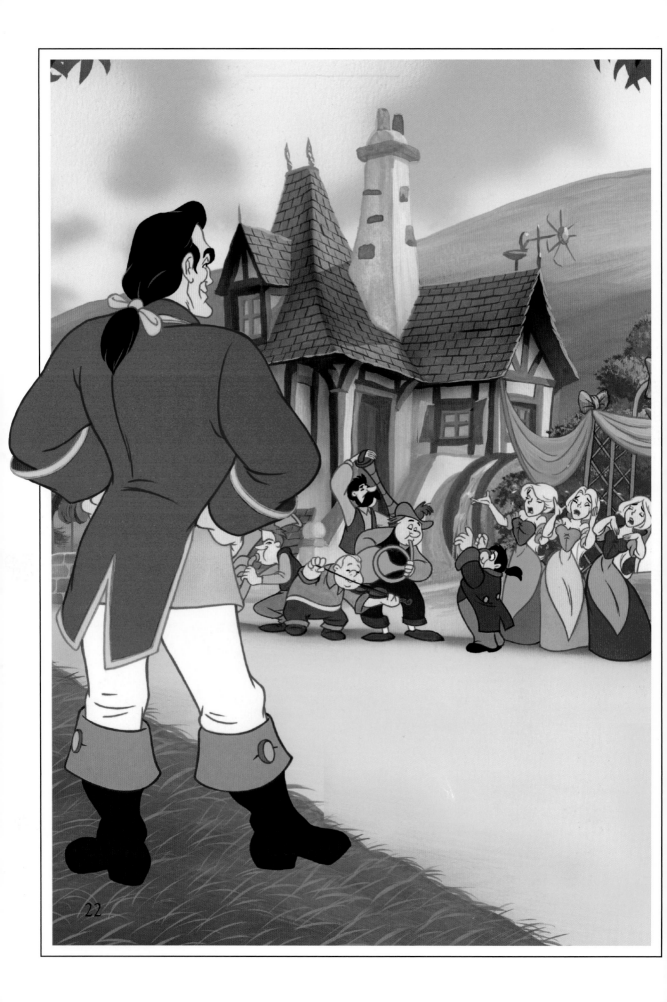

At that very moment, Gaston had arrived at Belle's house to propose marriage. A crowd waited outside to celebrate.

"Say you'll marry me," he ordered. Belle refused. She did not like the conceited bully!

When the crowd had left, Philippe arrived, with no rider.

"Philippe! Where's Papa? You must take me to him!" cried Belle.

BELLE'S PROMISE

Belle rode through the forest, braving the thick fog and frightening sounds. Soon she saw the huge turrets and gates of the castle rising out of the mist.

When Belle entered the castle, she found her father locked in the dungeon. As they embraced, a voice boomed from the shadows.

"I am the master of this castle!" roared the Beast.

"Take me instead," Belle cried.

When Belle promised to stay with the Beast forever, he released Maurice.

31

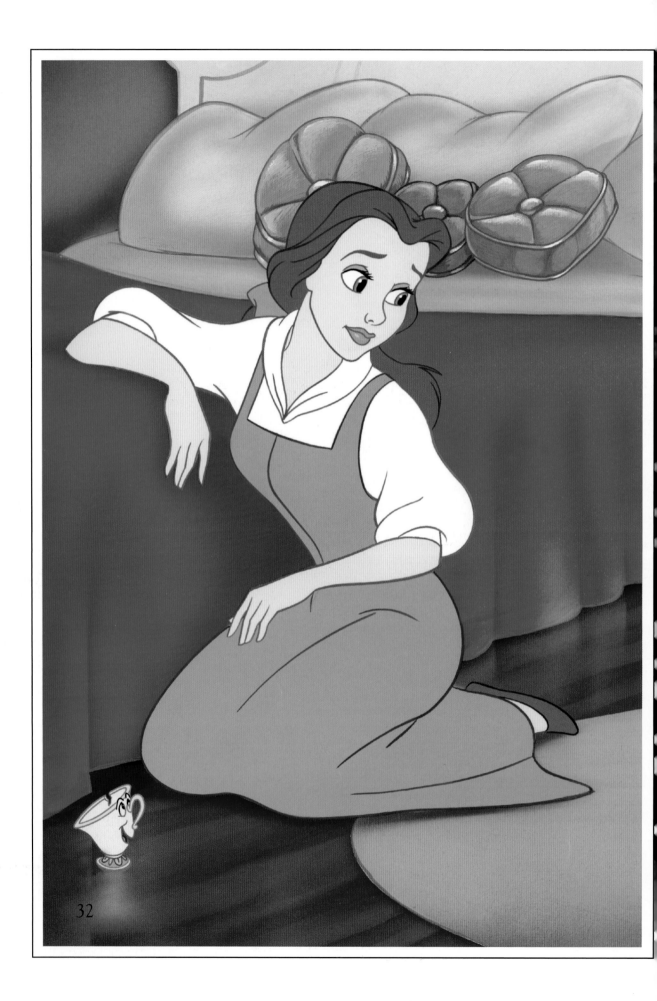

The Beast showed Belle to her room. "You can go anywhere you like . . . except the west wing. You'll join me for dinner," said the Beast and then he was gone.

Belle was angry at the Beast's unkind treatment. Not even Mrs. Potts, the friendly teapot, could cheer her up.

In the dining room, the Beast waited for Belle to join him for dinner.

"Master," said Lumiere, "this girl could be the one to break the spell! You fall in love and . . ."

"She'll always see me as a monster," grumbled the Beast.

Back in the village, Maurice begged for help to rescue Belle from a horrible beast. The crowd laughed, convinced that he was crazy.

But Gaston was thinking up a terrible plan.

38

At the castle, Belle had skipped dinner and was now hungry.

"Be our guest," said Lumiere, leading Belle to the dining room. Bottles popped their corks, dishes danced, and serving pieces carried in tasty food!

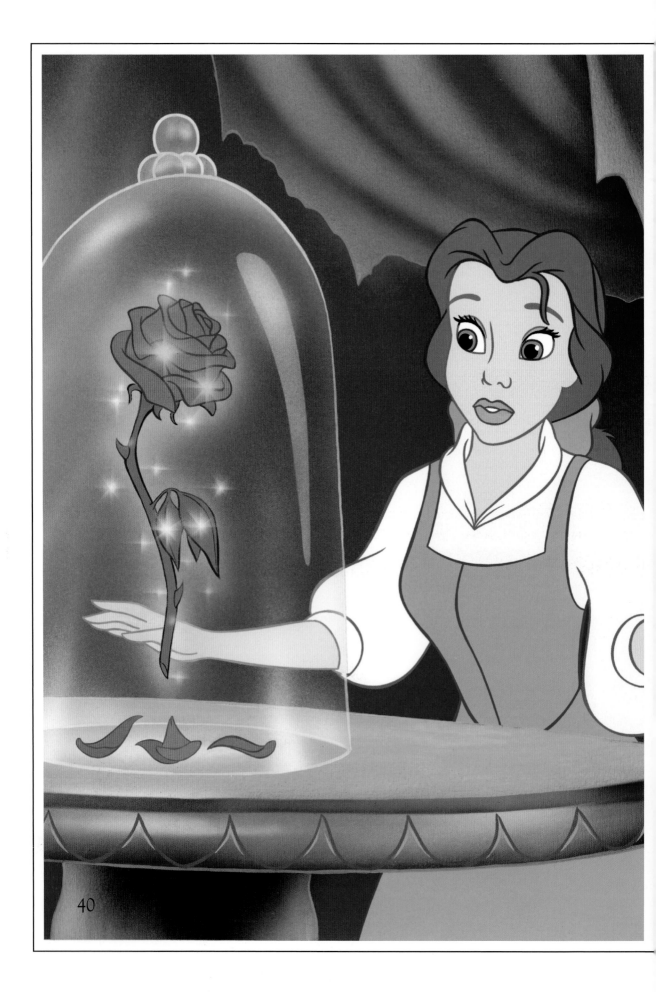

40

After dinner, Belle wandered into the forbidden west wing and found the enchanted rose.

She was about to touch it when the Beast shouted, "Get out!"

Terrified, Belle fled the castle and rode Philippe into the night.

Spooky yellow eyes glowed in the dark forest. The wolves were right behind them, lunging at Philippe's hooves. Belle was thrown off and tumbled into the snow. The wolf pack surrounded them!

Suddenly, a clawed hand
seized one of the wolves. It
was the Beast!

A wolf bit his arm and
the Beast threw him against
a tree. The pack retreated
into the darkness.

FRIENDSHIP BLOSSOMS

Belle and Philippe helped the injured Beast back to the castle.

Belle tended to the Beast's wound. "Thank you for saving my life," she said gently.

A friendship was blossoming between Belle and the Beast. At dinner, he tried to remember his manners. And later, they shared a wonderful dance. After they danced, the Beast asked Belle if she was happy.

"Yes," said Belle. "If only I could see my father."

The Beast brought Belle a magic mirror. When she wished to see her father, Maurice appeared in the glass, wandering lost in the forest.

"You must go to him. Take the mirror with you, so you can remember me," said the Beast sadly.

Belle left the castle. She brought her father home and lovingly cared for him. She told him about the Beast's kindness to her, and how he had let her go. Then there was a knock at the door.

Gaston had arrived with an angry crowd. "I'm here to take your crazy father to the asylum. He thinks he's seen a beast." Gaston would only release Maurice if Belle agreed to marry him.

When Belle used the magic mirror to show the Beast to the crowd, Gaston locked Belle and her father in their cellar. He set off to attack the Beast.

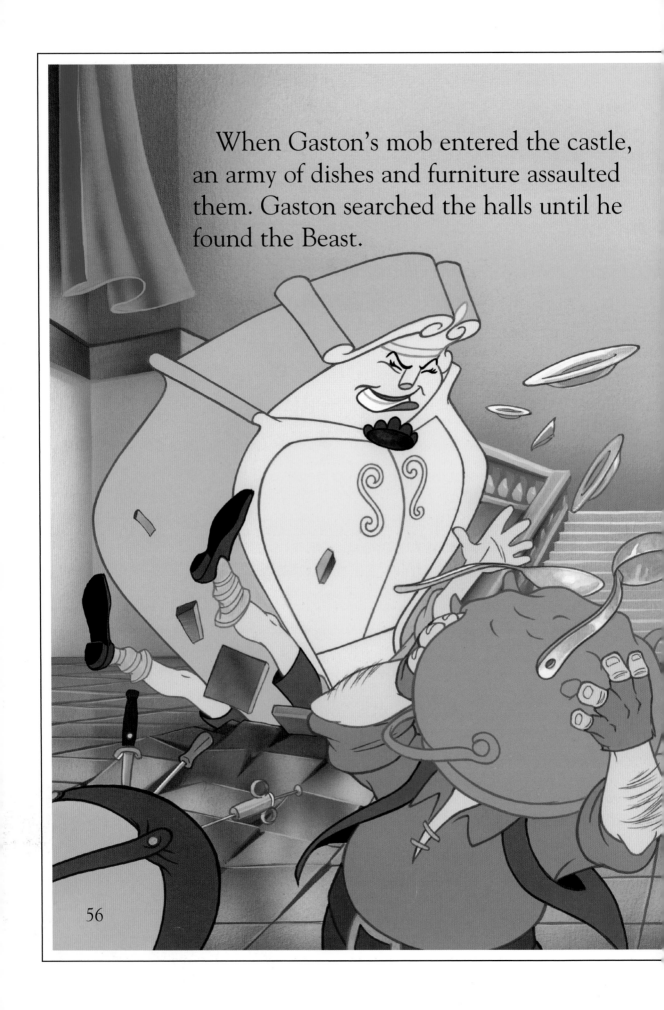

When Gaston's mob entered the castle, an army of dishes and furniture assaulted them. Gaston searched the halls until he found the Beast.

At that very moment, Belle escaped from
the cellar and began riding toward the castle!

Just as Belle and her father arrived, Gaston fired
an arrow at the Beast.

"No!" sobbed Belle. She charged into the castle
and ran up the stairs.

Belle had come back! With new hope, the Beast began to fight. When Belle reached them, the Beast had Gaston by the throat. "Let me go!" cried Gaston. The Beast felt sorry for Gaston and released him.

As the Beast embraced Belle, Gaston stabbed him
in the back! The Beast let out a terrible roar, and
Gaston tripped and fell off the balcony.
   The Beast collapsed in Belle's arms.

"You came back," said the Beast. "At least I got to see you one last time." Belle began to cry. In the Beast's room, the last rose petal was about to fall.

"No! Please . . . *please!*" said Belle. "I love you."

At Belle's words, the Beast's horrible claws turned into human hands, and his face grew smooth and fine.

The spell was broken! "Belle, it's me," said the Prince, and they embraced.

Joyfully, all the enchanted objects in the castle returned to their human forms.

And as Belle and her prince shared a wonderful dance, she knew that her dreams of romance and adventure had all come true.

The stones and shells of the deep channel
    Were in motion;
Swept from out their lowly bed
    By the tumult of the ocean;
Till the sea, like a great mess of pottage,
    Troubled, muddy grew
With the blood of many mangled creatures,
    Dirty red in hue –
When the horn'd and clawy wild beasts,
    Short-footed, splay,
With great wailing gumless mouths
    Huge and wide open lay.
But the whole deep was full of spectres,
    Loose and sprawling
With the claws and with the tails of monsters,
    Pawing, squalling.
It was frightful even to hear them
    Screech so loudly;
The sound might move full fifty heroes
    Stepping proudly.
Our whole crew grew dull of hearing
    In the tempest's scowl,
So sharp the quavering cries of demons
    And the wild beasts' howl.
With the oaken planks the weltering waves were wrestling
    In their noisy splashing;

While the sharp beak of our swift ship
    On the sea-pigs came dashing.
The wind kept still renewing all its wildness
    In the far West,
Till with every kind of strain and trouble
    We were sore distress'd.
We were blinded with the water
    Showering o'er us ever;
And the awful night like thunder,
    And the lightning ceasing never.
The bright fireballs in our tackling
    Flamed and smoked;
With the smell of burning brimstone
    We were well-nigh choked.
All the elements above, below,
    Against us wrought;
Earth and wind and fire and water,
    With us fought.
But when the evil one defied the sea
    To make us yield,
At last, with one bright smile of pity,
    Peace with us she seal'd:
Yet not before our yards were injured,
    And our sails were rent,
Our poops were strained, our oars were weaken'd,
    All our masts were bent.

Not a stay but we had started,
    Our tackling all was wet and splashy,
Nails and couplings, twisted, broken.
    Feeshie, fashie,
All the thwarts and all the gunwale
    Everywhere confess'd,
And all above and all below,
    How sore they had been press'd.
Not a bracket, not a rib,
    But the storm had loosed;
Fore and aft from stem to stern,
    All had got confused.
Not a tiller but was split,
    And the helm was wounded;
Every board its own complaint
    Sadly sounded.
Every trennel, every fastening
    Had been giving way;
Not a board remain'd as firm
    As at the break of day.
Not a bolt in her but started,
    Not a rope the wind that bore,
Not a part of the whole vessel
    But was weaker than before.
The sea spoke to us its peace prattle
    At the cross of Islay's Kyle,
And the rough wind, bitter boaster!
    Was restrained for one good while.

The tempest rose from off us into places
    Lofty in the upper air,
And after all its noisy barking
    Ruffled round us fair.
Then we gave thanks to the High King,
    Who rein'd the wind's rude breath,
And saved our good Clan Ranald
    From a bad and brutal death.
Then we furl'd up the fine and speckled sails
    Of linen wide,
And we took down the smooth red dainty masts,
    And laid them by the side –
On our long and slender polish'd oars
    Together leaning –
They were all made of the fir cut by Mac Barais
    In Eilean Fionain –
We went with our smooth, dashing rowing,
    And steady shock,
Till we reach'd the good port round the point
    Of Fergus' Rock.
There casting anchor peacefully
    We calmly rode;
We got meat and drink in plenty,
    And there we abode.

Alexander MacDonald
c.1700-1770

The Twa Corbies

As I was walking all alane,
I heard twa corbies making a mane; [1]
The tane[2] unto the t'other say,
'Where sall we gang[3] and dine to-day?'

'In behint yon auld fail dyke,[4]
I wot there lies a new slain knight;
And naebody kens that he lies there,
But his hawk, his hound, and lady fair.

'His hound is to the hunting gane,
His hawk to fetch the wild-fowl hame,
His lady's ta'en another mate,
So we may mak our dinner sweet.

'Ye'll sit on his white hause-bane,[5]
And I'll pike out his bonny blue een;
Wi ae lock o his gowden hair
We'll theek our nest when it grows bare.

'Mony a one for him makes mane,
But nane sall ken where he is gane;
Oer his white banes, when they are bare,
The wind sall blaw for evermair.'

Anon

1 moan   4 turf wall
2 the one   5 neck bone
3 go

11

Mountain Twilight

The hills slipped over each on each
    Till all their changing shadows died.
Now in the open skyward reach
    The lights grow solemn side by side.
While of these hills the westermost
Rears high his majesty of coast
    In shifting waste of dim-blue brine
    And fading olive hyaline;
Till all the distance overflows,
    The green in watchet and the blue
In purple. Now they fuse and close –
    A darkling violet, fringed anew
With light that on the mountains soar,
A dusky flame on tranquil shores;
    Kindling the summits as they grow
In audience to the skies that call,
Ineffable in rest and all
    The pathos of the afterglow.

William Renton
19th Century

Requiem

Under the wide and starry sky
Dig the grave and let me lie:
Glad did I live and gladly die,
　　And I laid me down with a will.

This be the verse you grave for me:
Here he lies where he long'd to be;
Home is the sailor, home from sea,
　　And the hunter home from the hill.

Robert Louis Stevenson
1850-1894

Lock the Door, Lariston

'Lock the door, Lariston, lion of Liddesdale;
Lock the door, Lariston, Lowther comes on;
    The Armstrongs are flying,
    The widows are crying'
The Castletown's burning, and Oliver's gone!

'Lock the door, Lariston - high on the weather gleam
See how the Saxon plumes bob on the sky -
    Yeomen and carbineer,
    Billman and halberdier,
Fierce is the foray, and far is the cry!

'Bewcastle brandishes high his broad scimitar;
Ridley is riding his fleet-footed grey;
    Hedley and Howard there,
    Wandale and Windermere;
Lock the door, Lariston; hold them at bay.

'Why dost thou smile, noble Elliot of Lariston?
Why does the joy-candle gleam in thine eye?
    Thou bold Border ranger,
    Beware of thy danger;
Thy foes are relentless, determined, and nigh.'

Jack Elliot raised up his steel bonnet and lookit,
His hand grasp'd the sword with a nervous embrace;
    'Ah, welcome, brave foemen,
    On earth there are no men
More gallant to meet in the foray or chase!

'Little know you of the hearts I have hidden here;
Little know you of our moss-troopers' might -
    Linhope and Sorbie true,
    Sundhope and Milburn too,
Gentle in manner, but lions in fight!

'I have Mangerton, Ogilvie, Raeburn, and Netherbie,
Old Sim of Whitram, and all his array;
    Come all Northumberland,
    Teesdale and Cumberland,
Here at the Breaken tower end shall the fray!'

Scowled the broad sun o'er the links of green Liddesdale,
Red as the beacon-light tipped he the wold;
    Many a bold martial eye
    Mirror'd that morning sky,
Never more oped on his orbit of gold.

Shrill was the bugle's note, dreadful the warrior's shout,
Lances and halberds in splinters were borne;
    Helmet and hauberk then
    Braved the claymore in vain,
Buckler and armlet in shivers were shorn.

See how they wane - the proud files of the Windermere!
Howard! ah, woe to thy hopes of the day!
    Hear the wide welkin rend,
    While the Scots' shouts ascend -
'Elliot of Lariston, Elliot for aye!'

James Hogg
1770-1835

Lochinvar

O, young Lochinvar is come out of the west,
Through all the wide Border his steed was the best;
And save his good broadsword he weapons had none,
He rode all unarm'd, and he rode all alone.
So faithful in love, and so dauntless in war,
There never was knight like the young Lochinvar.

He staid not for brake, and he stopp'd not for stone,
He swam the Eske river where ford there was none;
But ere he alighted at Netherby gate,
The bride had consented, the gallant came late:
For a laggard in love, and a dastard in war,
Was to wed the fair Ellen of brave Lochinvar.

So boldly he enter'd the Netherby Hall,
Among bride's-men, and kinsmen, and brothers, and all:
Then spoke the bride's father, his hand on his sword,
(For the poor craven bridegroom said never a word,)
'O come ye in peace here, or come ye in war,
Or to dance at our bridal, young Lord Lochinvar?'

'I long woo'd your daughter, my suit you denied; -
Love swells like the Solway, but ebbs like its tide -
And now am I come, with this lost love of mine,
To lead but one measure, drink one cup of wine.
There are maidens in Scotland more lovely by far,
That would gladly be bride to the young Lochinvar.'

The bride kiss'd the goblet; the knight took it up,
He quaff'd off the wine, and he threw down the cup.
She look'd down to blush, and she look'd up to sigh,
With a smile on her kips, and a tear in her eye.
He took her soft hand, ere her mother could bar, -
'Now tread we a measure!' said young Lochinvar.

So stately his form, and so lovely her face,
That never a hall such a galliard did grace;
While her mother did fret, and her father did fume,
And the bridegroom stood dangling his bonnet and plume;
And the bride-maidens whisper'd, 'Twere better by far,
To have match'd our fair cousin with young Lochinvar.'

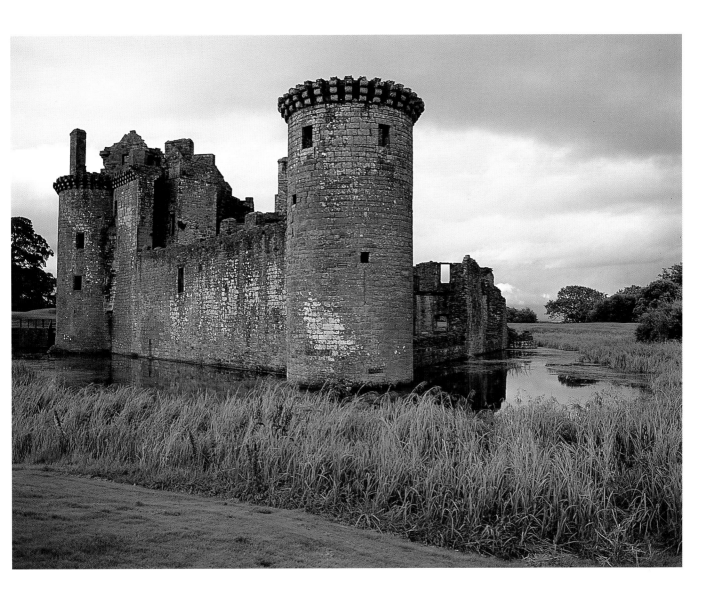

One touch to her hand, and one word in her ear,
When they reach'd the hall-door, and the charger stood near;
So light to the croupe the fair lady he swung,
So light to the saddle before her he sprung!
'She is won! we are gone, over bank, bush, and scaur;
They'll have fleet steeds that follow,' quoth young Lochinvar.

There was mounting 'mong Graemes of the Netherby clan;
Forsters, Fenwicks, and Musgraves, they rode and they ran:
There was racing and chasing on Cannobie Lee,
But the lost bride of Netherby ne'er did they see.
So daring in love, and so dauntless in war,
Have ye e'er heard of gallant like young Lochinvar?

Sir Walter Scott
1771-1832

Arran

Arran of the many stags,
the sea reaches to its shoulder;
island where companies are fed,
ridges whereon blue spears are reddened.

Wanton deer upon its peaks,
Mellow blaeberries on its heaths,
cold water in its streams,
mast upon its brown oaks.

Hunting dogs there, and hounds,
blackberries and sloes of the dark blackthorn,
dense thorn-bushes in its woods,
stags astray among its oak-groves.

Gathering of purple lichen on its rocks,
grass without blemish on its slopes;
over its fair shapely crags
gambolling of dappled fawns leaping.

Smooth is its lowland, fat are its swine,
pleasant its fields, a tale to be believed;
its nuts on the boughs of its hazel-wood,
sailing of long galleys past it.

It is delightful when fine weather comes,
trout under the banks of its streams,
seagulls answer each other round its white cliff;
delightful at all times is Arran.

Anon, translated from the Irish by Kenneth Jackson

His Metrical Prayer
(On the Eve of his Own Execution)

Let them bestow on ev'ry Airth[1] a Limb;
Open all my veins, that I may swim
To Thee my Saviour, in that Crimson Lake;
Then place my par-boiled Head upon a Stake;
Scatter my Ashes, throw them in the Air:
Lord (since Thou know'st where all these Atoms are)
I'm hopeful, once Thou'lt recollect my Dust,
And confident Thou'lt raise me with the Just.

James Graham
Marquis of Montrose
1612-1650

[1] north, south, east and west

In Shadowland

Between the moaning of the mountain stream
And the hoarse thunder of the Atlantic deep,
An outcast from the peaceful realms of sleep
I lie, and hear as in a fever-dream
The homeless night-wind in the darkness scream
And wail around the inaccessible steep
Down whose gaunt sides the spectral torrents leap
From crag to crag, - till almost I could deem
The plaided ghosts of buried centuries
Were mustering in the glen with bow and spear
And shadowy hounds to hunt the shadowy deer,
Mix in phantasmal sword-play, or, with eyes
Of wrath and pain immortal, wander o'er
Loved scenes where human footstep comes no more.

Sir Noel Paton
Born 1821

The Reed-Player

By a dim shore where water darkening
    Took the last light of spring,
I went beyond the tumult, harkening
    For some diviner thing.

Where the bats flew from the black elms like leaves,
    Over the ebon pool
Brooded the bittern's cry, as one that grieves
    Lands ancient, bountiful.

I saw the fire-flies shine below the wood,
    Above the shallows dank,
As Uriel, from some great altitude,
    The planets rank on rank.

And now unseen along the shrouded mead
    One went under the hill;
He blew a cadence on his mellow reed,
    That trembled and was still.

It seemed as if a line of amber fire
    Had shot the gathered dusk,
As if had blown a wind from ancient Tyre
    Laden with myrrh and musk.

He gave his luring note amid the fern;
    Its enigmatic fall
Haunted the hollow dusk with golden turn
    And argent interval.

I could not know the message that he bore,
    The springs of life from me
Hidden; his incommunicable lore
    As much a mystery.

And as I followed far the magic player
    He passed the maple wood;
And, when I passed, the stars had risen there,
    And there was solitude.

Duncan Campbell-Scott
19th Century

Venus and Cupid

Frae bank to bank, frae wood to wood I rin
Owrhailit[1] with my feeble fantasie,
Like til a leaf that fallis from a tree,
Or til a reed owrblawin with the wind.
Twa gods guides me: the ane of them is blin,
Yea, and a bairn brocht up in vanitie;
The nixt a wife ingenerit[2] of the sea
And lichter nor a dauphin[3] with her fin.

Unhappie is the man for evermair
That tills the sand and sawis in the air;
But twice unhappier is he, I lairn,
That feedis in his hairt a mad desire,
And follows on a woman throu the fire,
Led by a blin, and teachit by a bairn.

Mark Alexander Boyd
1563-1601

1 overwhelmed
2 born of
3 dolphin

The wee, wee German Lairdie

Wha the deil hae we got for a King,
  But a wee, wee German lairdie![1]
An' whan we gaed to bring him hame,
  He was delving in his kail-yardie.[2]
Sheughing[3] kail an' laying leeks,
  But[4] the hose and but the breeks,
Up his beggar duds[5] he cleeks,
  The wee, wee German lairdie.

An' he's clapt down in our gudeman's[6] chair,
  The wee, wee German lairdie;
An' he's brought fouth[7] o' foreign leeks,
  An' dibblet them in his yardie.
He's pu'd the rose o' English louns,[8]
  An' brak the harp o' Irish clowns,
But our thistle will jag his thumbs,
  The wee, wee German lairdie.

Come up amang the Highland hills,
  Thou wee, wee German lairdie;
An' see how Charlie's lang-kail[9] thrive,
  He dibblet in his yardie.
An' if a stock ye daur[10] to pu',
  Or haud[11] the yoking of a pleugh,
We'll break yere sceptre o'er yere mou',
  Thou wee bit German lairdie.

Our hills are steep, our glens are deep,
  Nae fitting for a yardie;
An' our norlan' thistles winna pu'
  Thou wee, wee German lairdie.
An' we've the trenching blades o' weir,[12]
  Wad twine ye o' yere German gear
An' pass ye 'neath the claymore's shear,
  Thou feckless[13] German lairdie.

1 minor squire	5 rags	9 swords of Prince	12 war
2 cabbage patch	6 king	Charles Edward's men	13 useless
3 picking	7 many	10 dare	
4 without	8 fellows	11 hold	

Allan Cunningham
1784-1842

To His Mistress

So sweet a kiss yestreen frae thee I reft,
In bowing doun thy body on the bed,
That even my life within thy lips I left.
Sensyne[1] from thee my spirits wald never shed.
To follow thee it from my body fled
And left my corpse als cold as ony key.
But when the danger of my death I dread,
To seek my spreit I sent by hairt to thee;
But it was so enamoured with thine ee,
With thee it mindit likewise to remain.
So thou hes keepit captive all the three,
More glaid to bide than to return again.
     Except thy breath their places had suppleit,
     Even in thine armes, there doutless had I deit.

Alexander Montgomerie
c.1545-c.1610

1 since then

The Hill-Water

From the rim it trickles down
Of the mountains granite crown clear and cool;
Keen and eager though it go
Through your veins with lively flow,
Yet it knoweth not to reign
In the chambers of the brain with misrule;

Where dark watercresses grow
You will trace its quiet flow,
With mossy border yellow,
So mild and soft, and mellow, in its pouring.
With no shiny dregs to trouble
The brightness of its bubble
As it threads its silver way
From the granite shoulders grey of Ben Dorain.

Then down the sloping side
It will leap with glassy slide gently welling
Till it gather strength to leap,
With a light and foamy sweep,
To the corrie broad and deep
Proudly swelling;

Then bends amid the boulders
'Neath the shadow of the shoulders of the Ben,
Through a country rough and shaggy,
So jaggy and so knaggy,
Full of hummocks and of hunches,
Full of stumps and tufts and bunches,
Full of bushes and of rushes, in the glen,

Through rich green solitudes,
And wildly hanging woods
With blossom and with bell,
In rich redundant swell, and the pride
Of the mountain daisy there, and the forest everywhere,
With the dress and with the air of a bride.

Duncan Ban MacIntyre
1724-1808

McLean's Welcome

Come o'er the stream, Charlie, dear Charlie, brave Charlie;
Come o'er the stream, Charlie, and dine with McLean;
And though you be weary, we'll make you heart cheery,
And welcome our Charlie, and his loyal train.
We'll bring down the track deer, we'll bring down the black steer,
The lamb from the braken, and doe from the glen,
The salt sea we'll harry, and bring to our Charlie
The cream from the bothy and curd from the pen.

Come o'er the stream, Charlie, dear Charlie, brave Charlie;
Come o'er the stream, Charlie, and dine with McLean;
And you shall drink freely the dews of Glen-Sheerly,
That stream in the starlight when kings do not ken,
And deep be your meed of the wine that is red,
To drink to your sire, and his friend the McLean.

Come o'er the stream, Charlie, dear Charlie, brave Charlie;
Come o'er the stream, Charlie, and dine with McLean;
O'er heath-bells shall trace you the maids to embrace you,
And deck your blue bonnet with flowers of the brae;
And the loveliest Mari in all Glen M'Quarry
Shall lie in your bosom till break of the day.

Come o'er the stream, Charlie, dear Charlie, brave Charlie;
Come o'er the stream, Charlie, and dine with McLean;
If aught will invite you, or more will delight you,
'Tis ready, a troop of our bold Highlandmen,
All ranged on the heather, with bonnet and feather,
Strong arms and broad claymores, three hundred and ten!

James Hogg
1770-1835

Scots, Wha Hae

Scots, wha hae wi'[1] Wallace bled,
Scots, wham Bruce has aften[2] led,
Welcome to your gory bed
    Or to victorie!

Now's the day, and now's the hour:
See the front o' battle lour,[3]
See approach proud Edward's power -
    Chains and slaverie!

Wha will be a traitor knave?
Wha can fill a coward's grave?
Wha sae base as be a slave?
    Let him turn and flee!

Wha for Scotland's King and Law
Freedom's sword will strongly draw,
Freeman stand, or freeman fa',
    Let him follow me!

By Oppression's woes and pains,
By your sons in servile chains,
We will drain our dearest veins
    But they shall be free!

Lay the proud usurpers low!
Tyrants fall in every foe!
Liberty's in every blow!
    Let us do, or die!

1 who have with
2 often
3 loom up

Robert Burns 1759-1796

The Lament of the Deer
(Cumha nam Fiadh)

O for my strength! once more to see the hills!
The wilds of Strath-Farar of stags,
The blue streams, and winding vales,
Where the flowering tree sends forth its sweet perfume.

My thoughts are sad and dark! -
I lament the forest where I loved to roam,
The secret corries, the haunt of hinds,
Where often I watched them on the hill!

Corrie-Garave! O that I was within thy bosom
Scuir-na-Lapàich of steeps, with thy shelter,
Where feed the herds which never seek for stalls,
But whose skin gleams red in the sunshine of the hills.

Great was my love in youth, and strong my desire,
Towards the bounding herds;
But now, broken, and weak, and hopeless,
Their remembrance wounds my heart.

To linger in the laich[1] I mourn,
My thoughts are ever in the hills;
For there my childhood and my youth was nursed -
The moss and the craig in the morning breeze was my delight.

Then was I happy in my life,
When the voices of the hill sung sweetly;
More sweet to me, than any string,
It soothed my sorrow or rejoiced my heart.

My thoughts wandered to no other land
Beyond the hill of the forest, the shealings of the deer,
Where the nimble herds ascended the hill, -
As I lay in my plaid on the dewy bed.

The sheltering hollows, where I crept towards the hart,
On the pastures of the glen, or in the forest wilds -
And if once more I may see them as of old,
How will my heart bound to watch again the pass!

Great was my joy to ascend the hills
In the cause of the noble chief,
Mac Shimé of the piercing eye - never to fail at need,
With all his brave Frasers, gathered beneath his banner.

When they told of his approach, with all his ready arms,
My heart bounded for the chase -
On the rugged steep, on the broken hill,
By hollow, and ridge, many were the red stags which he laid low.

He is the pride of hunters; my trust was in his gun,
When the sound of its shot rung in my ear,
The great ball launched in flashing fire,
And the dun stag fell in the rushing speed of his course.

When evening came down on the hill,
The time for return to the star of the glen,
The kindly lodge where the noble gathered,
The sons of the tartan and the plaid,

With joy and triumph they returned
To the dwelling of plenty and repose;
The bright blazing hearth - the circling wine -
The welcome of the noble chief!

Angus MacKenzie
published 1848

1 Low country

O my luve's like a red, red rose

O my luve's like a red, red rose,
    That's newly sprung in June:
O my luve's like the melodie
    That's sweetly play'd in tune.

As fair art thou, my bonnie lass,
    So deep in luve am I;
And I will luve thee still, my dear,
    Till a' the seas gang dry.

Till a' the seas gang dry, my dear,
    And the rocks will melt wi' the sun;
And I will luve thee still, my dear,
    While the sands o' life shall run.

And fare thee weel, my only luve!
    And fare thee weel a while!
And I will come again, my luve,
    Tho' it were ten thousand mile.

Robert Burns
1759-1796

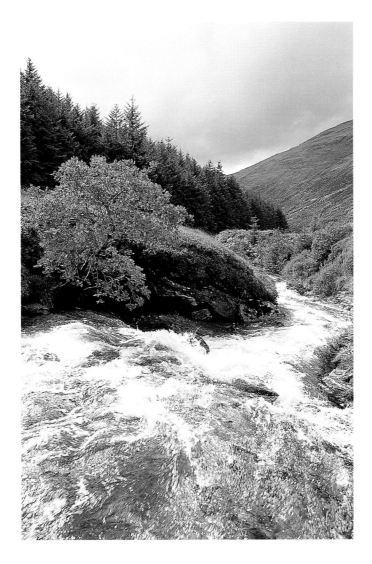

Durisdeer

We'll meet nae mair at sunset when the weary day is dune,
Nor wander hame thegither by the lee licht o' the mune.
I'll hear your steps nea langer amang the dewy corn,
For we'll meet nae mair, my bonniest, either at e'en or morn.

The yellow broom is waving abune the sunny brae,
And the rowan berries dancing where the sparkling waters play;
Tho' a' is bright and bonnie it's an eerie place to me,
For we'll meet nae mair, my dearest, either by burn or tree.

Far up into the wild hills there's a kirkyard lone and still,
Where the frosts lie ilka morning and the mists hang low and chill.
And there ye sleep in silence while I wander here my lane
Till we meet ance mair in Heaven never to part again!

Lady John Scott
19th Century

Thomas the Rhymer

True Thomas lay on Huntlie bank;
    A ferlie he spied wi' his e'e;
And there he saw a ladye bright
    Come riding down by the Eildon Tree.

Her skirt was o' the grass-green silk,
    Her mantle o' the velvet fyne;
At ilka tett o' her horse's mane
    Hung fifty siller bells and nine.

True Thomas he pu'd aff his cap,
    And louted low down on his knee:
'Hail to thee, Mary, Queen of Heaven!
    For thy peer on earth could never be.'

'O no, O no, Thomas,' she said
    'That name does not belang to me;
I'm but the Queen o' fair Elfland,
    That am hither come to visit thee.

'Harp and carp, Thomas,' she said;
    'Harp and carp along wi' me;
And if ye dare to kiss my lips,
    Sure of your bodie I will be.'

'Betide me weal, betide me woe,
    That weird shall never daunten me.'
Syne he has kiss'd her rosy lips,
    All underneath the Eildon Tree.

'Now ye maun go wi' me,' she said,
    'True Thomas, ye maun go wi' me;
And ye maun serve me seven years,
    Thro' weal or woe as may chance to be.'

She's mounted on her milk-white steed,
    She's ta'en true Thomas up behind;
And aye, whene'er her bridle rang,
    The steed gaed swifter that the wind.

O they rade on, and farther on,
    The steed gaed swifter than the wind;
Until they reach'd a desert wide,
    And living land was left behind.

'Light down, light down now, true Thomas,
    And lean your head upon my knee;
Abide ye there a little space,
    And I will show you ferlies three.

'O see ye not yon narrow road,
      So thick beset wi' thorns and briers?
That is the Path of Righteousness,
      Though after it but few inquires.

'And see ye not yon braid, braid road,
      That lies across the lily leven?
That is the Path of Wickedness,
      Though some call it the Road to Heaven.

'And see ye not yon bonny road
      That winds about the fernie brae?
That is the road to fair Elfland,
      Where thou and I this night might maun
                                    gae.

'But, Thomas, ye sall haud your tongue,
      Whatever ye may hear or see;
For speak ye word in Elfyn-land,
      Ye'll ne'er win back to your ain countrie.'

O they rade on, and farther on,
      And they waded river abune the knee;
And they saw neither sun nor moon,
      But they heard the roaring of the sea.

It was mirk, mirk night, there was nae starlight,
      They waded thro' red blude to the knee;
For a' the blude that's shed on the earth
      Rins through the springs o' that countrie.

Syne they came to a garden green,
      And she pu'd an apple frae a tree:
'Take this for thy wages, true Thomas;
      It will give thee the tongue that can never lee.'

'My tongue us my ain,' true Thomas he said;
      'A gudely gift ye wad gie to me!
I neither dought to buy or sell
      At fair or tryst where I might be.

'I dought neither speak to prince or peer,
      Nor ask of grace from fair ladye!' -
'Now haud thy peace, Thomas,'she said,
      "For as I say, so must it be.'

He has gotten a coat of even cloth,
      And a pair o' shoon of the velvet green;
And till seven years were gane and past,
      True Thomas on earth was never seen.

Anonymous

The Hind is in the Forest

The hind is in the forest
as she ought to be,
where she may have sweet grass,
clean, fine-bladed;
    heath-rush and deer's hair grass
    herbs in which strength resides,
    and which would make her flanks
    plump and fat-covered;
    a spring in which there is
    adundant water-cress,
    she deems more sweet than wine,
    and would drink of it;
    sorrel and rye grass
    which flourish on the moor,
    she prefers as food
    to rank field grass.

Of her fare she deemed
these the delicacies:
primrose, St John's wort
and tormentil flowers;
    tender spotted orchis,
    forked, spiked and glossy,
    on meadows where, in clusters,
    it flourishes.
    Such was the dietary
    that would increase their strength,
    that would pull them through
    in the stormy days;
    that would upon their back
    amass the roll of fat,
    which, over their spare frame,
    was not cumbersome.

That was a comely fellowship
at eventide,
when they would assemble
in the gloaming:
     though long the night might be
     no harm would come to you;
     the lee base of the knoll
     was your dwelling place.
     Here are the beds of deer,
     where they have ever been,
     on a spacious, bounteous moor,
     and on mountain range.
     Delightful was their hue,
     when vivid was their hide;
     'twas no mean portion they desired,
     it was Ben Dobhrain.

Duncan Ban MacIntyre
1724-1808

To S. R. Crockett
(On receiving a Dedication)

Blows the wind today, and the sun and the rain are flying,
    Blows the wind on the moors today and now,
Where about the graves of the martyrs the whaups[1] are crying,
    My heart remembers how!

Grey recumbent tombs of the dead in desert places,
    Standing-stones on the vacant wine-red moor,
Hills of sheep, and the howes[2] of the silent vanished races,
    And winds, austere and pure.

Be it granted me to behold you again in dying,
    Hills of home! and to hear again the call;
Hear about the graves of the martyrs the peewees[3] crying,
    And hear no more at all.

Robert Louis Stevenson
1850-1894

1 curlews
2 hollows, glens
3 lapwings

The Highland Crofter

Frae Kenmore tae Ben More
The land is a' the Marquis's;
The mossy howes, the heathery knowes
An' ilka bonnie park is his;
The bearded goats, the towsie stots,
An' a' the braxie carcases;
Ilk crofter's rent, ilk tinkler's tent,
An ilka collie's bark is his;
The muir-cock's craw, the piper's blaw,
The ghillie's hard day's wark is his;
Frae Kenmore tae Ben More
The warld is a' the Marquis's.

The fish that swim, the birds that skim,
The fir, the ash, the birk is his;
The Castle ha' sae big and braw,
Yon diamond-crusted dirk is his;
The roofless hame, a burning shame,

The factor's dirty wark is his;
The poor folk vexed, the lawyer's text,
Yon smirking legal shark is his;
Frae Kenmore tae Ben More
The warld is a' the Marquis's.
But near, mair near, God's voice we hear -
The dawn as weel's the dark is His;
The poet's dream, the patriot's theme,
The fire that lights the mirk is His.
They clearly show God's mills are slow
But sure the handiwork is His;
And in His grace our hope we place;
Fair Freedom's sheltering ark is His.
The men that toil should own the soil -
A note as clear's the lark is this -
Breadalbane's land - the fair, the grand -
Will no' be aye the Marquis's.

Anonymous

The Last Journey
(From *The Testament of John Davidson*)

I felt the world a-spinning on its nave,
 I felt it sheering blindly round the sun;
I felt the time had come to find a grave:
 I knew it in my heart my days were done.
I took my staff in hand; I took the road,
And wandered out to seek my last abode.
  Hearts of gold and hearts of lead
  Sing it yet in sun and rain
  'Heel and toe from dawn to dusk,
  Round the world and home again.'

O long before the bere was steeped for malt,
 And long before the grape was crushed for wine,
The glory of the march without a halt,
 The triumph of a stride like yours and mine
Was known to folk like us, who walked about,
To be the sprightliest cordial out and out!
  Folk like us, with hearts that beat
  Sang it too in sun and rain
  'Heel and toe from dawn to dusk,
  Round the world and home again.'

My feet are heavy now, but on I go,
 My head erect beneath the tragic years.
The way is steep, but I would have it so;
 And dusty, but I lay the dust with tears,
Though none can see me weep: alone I climb
The rugged path that leads me out of time -
  Out of time and out of all,
  Singing yet in sun and rain
  'Heel and toe from dawn to dusk,
  Round the world and home again.'

Farewell the hope that mocked, farewell despair
 That went before me still and made the pace.
The earth is full of graves, and mine was there
 Before my life began, my resting-place;
And I shall find it out and with the dead
Lie down for ever, all my sayings said -
  Deeds all done and songs all sung,
  While others chant in sun and rain,
  'Heel and toe from dawn to dusk,
  Round the world and home again.'

John Davidson
1857-1909

The Tryst

O luely, luely, cam she in
And luely she lay doun:
I kent her be her caller lips
And her briests sae sma' and roun'.

A' thru the nicht we spak nae word
Nor sinder'd bane frae bane:
A' thru the nicht I heard her hert
Gang soundin' wi' my ain.

It was about the waukrife hour
Whan cocks begin to craw
That she smool'd saftly thru the mirk
Afore the day wud daw.

Sae luely, luely, cam she in
Sae luely was she gaen;
And wi' her a' my simmer days
Like they had never been.

William Soutar
1898-1943

Bonny Kilmeny gaed up the Glen

Bonny Kilmeny gaed up the glen,
But it wasna to meet Duneira's men,
Nor the rosy monk on the isle to see,
For Kilmeny was pure as pure could be.
It was only to hear the yorlin sing,
And pu' the cress-flower round the spring;
The scarlet hypp and the hindberrye,
And the nut that hung frae the hazel tree;
For Kilmeny was as pure as pure could be.
But lang may her minny look o'er the wa',
And lang may she seek i' the green-wood shaw;
Lang the laird of Duneira blame,
And lang, lang greet or Kilmeny come hame!

When many a day had come and fled,
When grief grew calm, and hope was dead,
When mass for Kilmeny's soul had been sung,
When the bedes-man had prayed, and the dead bell rung,
Late, late in a gloamin' when all was still,

When the fringe was red on the westlin hill,
The wood was sere, the moon i' the wane,
The reek o' the cot hung over the plain,
Like a little wee cloud in the world its lane;
When the ingle lowed with an eiry leme,
Late, late in the gloamin' Kilmeny came hame!
'Kilmeny, Kilmeny, where have you been?
Lang hae we sought baith holt and dean;
By linn, by ford, and green-wood tree,
Yet you are halesome and fair to see.
Where gat you that joup o' the lily schene?
That bonny snood of the birk sae green?
And these roses, the fairest that ever were seen?
Kilmeny, Kilmeny, where have you been?'

Kilmeny looked up with a lovely grace,
But nae smile was seen on Kilmeny's face;
As still was her look, and as still was her ee,
As the stillness that lay on the emerant lea,

Or the mist that sleeps on a waveless sea.
For Kilmeny had been she knew not where,
And Kilmeny had seen what she could not declare;
Kilmeny had been where the cock never crew,
Where the rain never fell, and the wind never blew;
But it seemed as the harp of the sky had rung,
And the airs of heaven played round her tongue,
When she spake of the lovely forms she had seen,
And a land where sin had never been;
A land of love, and a land of light,
Withouten sun, or moon, or night;
Where the river swa'd a living stream,
And the light a pure celestial beam:
The land of vision it would seem,
A still, an everlasting dream...
When seven lang years had come and fled;
When grief was calm, and hope was dead;
When scarce was remembered Kilmeny's name,
Late, late in a gloamin' Kilmeny came home!

James Hogg
1770-1835

Skye

My heart is yearning to thee, O Skye!
    Dearest of Islands!
There first the sunshine gladdened my eye,
    On the sea sparkling;
There doth the dust of my dear ones lie,
    In the old graveyard.

Bright are the golden green fields to me,
    Here in the Lowlands;
Sweet sings the mavis in the thorn-tree,
    Snowy with fragrance:
But oh for a breath of the great North Sea,
    Girdling the mountains!

Good is the smell of the brine that laves
    Black rock and skerry,
Where the great palm-leaved tangle waves
    Down in the green depths,
And round the craggy bluff pierced with caves
    Sea-gulls are screaming.

When the sun sinks below Humish Head,
    Crowning in glory,
As he goes down to his ocean bed
    Studded with islands,
Flushing the Coolin with royal red,
    Would I were sailing!

Many a hearth round that friendly shore
    Giveth warm welcome;
Charms still are there, as in days of yore,
    More than of mountains;
But hearths and faces are seen no more
    Once of the brightest.

Many a poor black cottage is there,
    Grimy with peat smoke,
Sending up in the soft evening air
    Purest blue incense,
While the low music of psalm and prayer
    Rises to Heaven.

Kind were the voices I used to hear
    Round such a fireside,
Speaking the mother tongue old and dear,
    Making the heart beat
With sudden tales of wonder and fear,
    Or plaintive singing.

Reared in those dwellings have brave ones been;
    Brave ones are still there;
Forth from their darkness on Sunday I've seen
    Coming pure linen,
And like the linen the souls were clean
    Of them that wore it.

See that thou kindly use them, O man!
    To whom God giveth
Stewardship over them, in thy short span
    Not for thy pleasure;
Woe be to them who choose for a clan
    Four-footed people!

Great were the marvellous stories told
    Of Ossian's heroes,
Giants, and witches, and young men bold,
    Seeking adventures,
Winning kings' daughters and guarded gold,
    Only with valour.

Blessings be with ye, both now and aye
    Dear human creatures!
Yours is the love that no gold can buy!
    Nor time wither
Peace be to thee and thy children, O Skye!
    Dearest of islands.

Alexander Nicolson
19th Century

Canadian Boat Song

Fair these broad meads - these hoary woods are grand;
    But we are exiles from our fathers' land.

Listen to me, as when ye heard our father
    Sing long ago the song of other shores -
Listen to me, and then in chorus gather
    All your deep voices, as ye pull your oars.

From the lone shieling[1] of the misty island
    Mountains divide us, and waste of seas -
Yet still the blood is strong, the heart is Highland,
    And we in dreams behold the Hebrides.

We ne'er shall tread the fancy-haunted valley,
    Where 'tween the dark hills creeps the small clear stream,
In arms around the patriarch banner rally,
    Nor see the moon on royal tombstones gleam.

When the bold kindred, in the time long vanish'd,
    Conquer'd the soil and fortified the keep -
No seer foretold the children would be banish'd.
    That a degenerate lord might boast his sheep.

Come foreign rage - let Discord burst in slaughter!
    O then for clansmen true, and stern claymore
The hearts that would have given their blood like water,
    Beat heavily beyond the Atlantic roar.

Anonymous
18th Century

1 upland cottage

44

In the Highlands

In the highlands, in the country places,
Where the old plain men have rosy faces,
And the young fair maidens
    Quiet eyes;
Where essential silence cheers and blesses,
And for ever in the hill-recesses
Her more lovely music
    Broods and dies.

O to mount again where erst I haunted;
Where the old red hills are bird-enchanted,
And the low green meadows
    Bright with sward;

And when even dies, the million-tinted,
And the night has come, and planets glinted,
Lo, the valley hollow
    Lamp-bestarred!

O to dream, O to wake and wander
There, and with delight to take and render,
Through the trance of silence
    Quiet breath;
Lo! for there, among the flowers and grasses,
Only the mightier movement sounds and passes;
Only winds and river,
    Life and death.

Robert Louis Stevenson
1850-1894

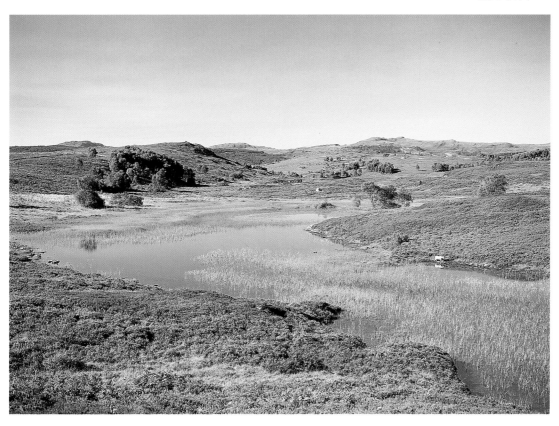

Lyric from 'The Crier by Night'

The bird in my heart's a-calling through a far-fled, tear-grey sea
To the soft slow hills that cherish dim waters weary for me,
Where the folk of rath and dun trail homeward silently
In the mist of the early night-fall that drips from their hair like rain.

The bird in my heart's a-flutter, for the bitter wind of the sea
Shivers with thyme and woodbine as my body with memory;
I feel their perfumes ooze in my ears like melody -
The scent of the mead at the harping I shall not hear again.

The bird in my heart's a-sinking to a hushed vale hid in the sea,
Where the moonlit dew o'er dead fighters is stirred by the feet of the
                                                                    Shee,
Who are lovely and old as the earth but younger than I can be
Who have known the forgetting of dying to a life one lonely pain.

Gordon Bottomley
19th Century

The Dreary Change

The sun upon the Weirdlaw Hill,
    In Ettrick's vale, is sinking sweet;
The westland wind is hush and still,
    The lake lies sleeping at my feet.
Yet not the landscape to mine eye
    Bears those bright hues that once it bore;
Though evening, with her richest dye,
    Flames o'er the hills of Ettrick's shore.

With listless look along the plain
    I see Tweed's silver current glide,
And coldly mark the holy fane
    Of Melrose rise in ruin'd pride.
The quiet lake, the balmy air,
    The hill, the stream, the tower, the tree, -
Are they still such as once they were,
    Or is it the dreary change in me?

Alas, the warp'd and broken board,
    How can it bear the painter's dye!
The harp of strain'd and tuneless chord,
    How to the minstrel's skill reply!
To aching eyes each landscape lowers,
    To feverish pulse each gale blows chill;
And Araby's or Eden's bowers
    Were barren as this moorland hill.

Sir Walter Scott
1771-1832

My Heart's in the Highlands

My heart's in the Highlands, my heart is not here;
My heart's in the Highlands a chasing the deer;
Chasing the wild deer, and following the roe;
My heart's in the Highlands, wherever I go.

Farewell to the Highlands, farewell to the North;
The birth-place of valour, the country of worth:
Wherever I wander, wherever I rove,
The hills of the Highlands for ever I love.

Farewell to the mountains high cover'd with snow;
Farewell to the Straths and green valleys below:
Farewell to the forests and wild-hanging woods;
Farewell to the torrents and loud-pouring floods.

My heart's in the Highlands, my heart is not here,
My heart's in the Highlands a chasing the deer:
Chasing the wild deer, and following the roe;
My heart's in the Highlands, wherever I go.

Robert Burns
1759-1796

A Kiss of the King's Hand

It wasna from a golden throne,
Or a bower with milk-white roses blown,
But mid the kelp on northern sand
That I got a kiss of the King's hand.

I durstna raise my een to see
If he even cared to glance at me;
His princely brow with care was crossed
For his true men slain and kingdom lost.

Think not his hand was soft and white,
Or his fingers a' with jewels dight,
Or round his wrists were ruffles grand
When I got a kiss of the King's hand.

But dearer far to my twa een
Was the ragged sleeve of red and green
O'er that young weary hand that fain,
With the guid broadsword, had found its ain.

Farewell for ever, the distance grey
And the lapping ocean seemed to say -
For him a home in a foreign land.
And for me one kiss of the King's hand.

Sarah Robertson Matheson
poem appeared 1894

Go, Hart, Unto the Lamp of Licht

Go, hart, unto the lamp of licht.
    Go, hart, do service and honour,
Go, hart, and serve him day and nicht:
    Go, hart, unto thy Saviour.

Go, hart, to thy onlie remeid
    Descending from the hevinlie tour,
Thee to deliver from pain and deid;
    Go, hart, unto thy Saviour.

Go, hart, but[1] dissimulatioun,
    To Christ that tuke our wild nature
For thee to suffer passioun;
    Go, hart, unto thy Saviour.

Go, hart, richt humill and meek,
    Go, hart, as leil[2] and trew servitour
To him that heil[3] is for all seick;
    Go, hart, unto thy Saviour.

Go, hart, with trew and hail intent
    To Christ, thy help and hail succour;
Thee to redeem, He was all rent;
    Go, hart, unto thy Saviour.

To Christ, that raise from deith to live,
    Go, hart, unto my latter hour;
Whase great mercy can nane descrive;[4]
    Go, hart, unto thy Saviour.

Anonymous

1 without
2 trusty
3 healing
4 describe

Auld Lang Syne

Should auld acquaintance be forgot,
    And never brought to mind?
Should auld acquaintance be forgot
    And days o'lang syne?[1]

For auld lang syne, my jo,[2]
    For auld lang syne,
We'll tak a cup o' kindness yet
    For auld lang syne.

And surely you'll be your pint-stowp,[3]
    And surely I'll be mine,
And we'll tak a cup o' kindness yet
    For auld lang syne!

    For auld lang syne, etc

We twa hae run about the braes,
    And pu'd the gowans[4] fine,
But we've wander'd monie a weary fit[5]
    Sin' auld lang syne.

    For auld lang syne, etc

We twa hae paidl'd in the burn
    Frae morning sin til dine,
But seas between us braid[6] hae roar'd
    Sin' auld lang syne.

    For auld lang syne, etc

And there's a hand, my trusty fiere,
    And gie's a hand of thine,
And we'll tak a right guid-willie waught[7]
    For auld lang syne!

    For auld lang syne, etc

Robert Burns
1759-1796

1 former days
2 dear
3 tankard
4 daisies
5 foot
6 broad
7 friendly draught

Extract from 'The Dream of the World Without Death'

' I laid my little girl upon a wood-bier,
And very sweet she seemed, and near unto me;
And slipping flowers into her shroud was comfort.

I put my silver mother in the darkness,
And kissed her, and was solaced by her kisses,
And set a stone, to mark the place, above her.

And green, green were their quiet sleeping places,
So green that it was pleasant to remember
That I and my tall man would sleep beside them.

The closing of dead eyelids is not dreadful,
For comfort comes upon us when we close them,
And tears fall, and our sorrow grows familiar;

And we can sit above them where they slumber,
And spin a dreamy pain into a sweetness,
And know instead that we are very near to them.'

Robert Buchanan
born 1841

Ettrick Forest in November

November's sky is chill and drear,
November's leaf is red and sear:
Late, gazing down the steepy linn,
That hems our little garden in,
Low in its dark and narrow glen
You scarce the rivulet might ken,
So thick the tangled greenwood grew,
So feeble trill'd the streamlet through:
Now, murmuring hoarse, and frequent seen
Through bush and brier, no longer green,
An angry brook, it sweeps the glade,
Brawls over rock and wild cascade,
And, foaming brown with doubled speed,
Hurries its waters to the Tweed.

No longer Autumn's glowing red
Upon our Forest hills is shed;
No more beneath the evening beam
Fair Tweed reflects their purple gleam;

Away hath pass'd the heather-bell
That bloom'd so rich on Needpathfell;
Sallow his brow; and russet bare
Are now the sister-heights of Yair.
The sheep, before the pinching heaven,
To shelter'd dale and down are driven,
Where yet some faded herbage pines,
And yet a watery sunbeam shines:
In meek despondency they eye
The wither'd sward and wintry sky,
And far beneath their summer hill,
Stray sadly by Glenkinnon's rill:
The shepherd shifts his mantle's fold,
And wraps him closer from the cold;
His dogs no merry circles wheel,
But shivering follow at his heel;
A cowering glance they often cast,
As deeper moans the gathering blast.

Sir Walter Scott 1771-1832

Romance

I will make you brooches and toys for your delight
Of bird-song at morning and star-shine at night.
I will make a palace fit for you and me,
Of green days in forests and blue days at sea.

I will make my kitchen, and you shall keep your room,
Where white flows the river and bright blows the broom,
And you shall wash your linen and keep your body white
In rainfall at morning and dewfall at night.

And this shall be for music when no one else is near,
The fine song for singing, the rare song to hear!
That only I remember, that only you admire,
Of the broad road that stretches and the roadside fire.

Robert Louis Stevenson
1850-1894

Tam I' The Kirk

O Jean, my Jean, when the bell ca's the congregation,
Owre valley an' hill wi' the ding frae its iron mou',
When a' body's thochts is set on his ain salvation,
    Mine's set on you.

There's a reid rose lies on the Biuk o' the Word afore ye
That was growin' braw on its bush at the keek o' day,
But the lad that pu'd yon flower i' the mornin's glory
    He canna pray.

He canna pray; but there's nane i' the kirk will heed him
Whaur he sits his lane at the side o' the wa'.
For nane but the reid rose kens what my lassie gie'd him:
    It an' us twa!

He canna sing for the sang that his ain he'rt raises,
He canna see for the mist that's afore his een,
And a voice drouns the hale o' the psalms an' the paraphrases,
    Cryin' 'Jean, Jean, Jean!'

Violet Jacob
1863-1946

The Coolun

Come with me, under my coat,
And we will drink our fill
Of the milk of the white goat,
Or wine if it be thy will;
And we will talk until
Talk is a trouble, too,
Out on the side of the hill,
And nothing is left to do,
But an eye to look into an eye
And a hand in a hand to slip,

And a sigh to answer a sigh,
And a lip to find out a lip:
What if the night be black
And the air on the mountain chill,
Where the goat lies down in her track
And all but the fern is still!
Stay with me under my coat,
And we will drink our fill
Of the milk of the white goat
Out on the side of the hill.

James Stephens
19th Century

To the Sun

Greeting to you, sun of the seasons, as you travel the skies on high,
with your strong steps on the wing of the heights; you are the happy
mother of the stars.

   You sink down in the perilous ocean without harm and without
hurt, you rise up on the quiet wave like a young queen in flower.

Scottish Gaelic; traditional folk prayer

Monaltri

There's a sound on the hill,
    Not of joy but of ailing;
Dark-hair'd women mourn -
    Beat their hands, with loud wailing.

They cry out, Ochon!
    For the young Monaltri,
Who went to the hill;
    But home came not he.

Without snood, without plaid
    Katrina's gone roaming.
O Katrina, my dear!
    Homeward be coming.

Och! hear, on the castle
    Yon pretty bird singing,
'Snoodless and plaidless,
    Her hands she is ringing.'

Anonymous

58

My Own, my Native Land!

Breathes there the man with soul so dead,
Who never to himself hath said,
This is my own, my native land!
Whose heart hath ne'er within him burn'd
As home his footsteps he hath turn'd,
    From wandering on a foreign strand!
If such there breathe, go, mark him well;
For him no minstrel raptures swell;
High though his titles, proud his name,
Boundless his wealth as wish can claim;
Despite these titles, power, and pelf,
The wretch, concentred all in self,
Living, shall forfeit fair renown,
And, doubly dying, shall go down
To the vile dust, from whence he sprung,
Unwept, unhonour'd, and unsung.

O Caledonia! stern and wild,
Meet a nurse for a poetic child!
Land of brown heath and shaggy wood,
Land of the mountain and the flood,
Land of my sires! what mortal hand
Can e'er untie the filial band
That knits me to thy rugged strand?
Still, as I view each well-known scene,
Think of what is now, and what hath been,
Seems as, to me, of all bereft,
Sole friends thy woods and streams were
                    left;
And this I love them better still,
Even in extremity of ill.

Sir Walter Scott
1771-1832

Tak' Your Auld Cloak About Ye

In winter when the rain rain'd cauld,
        And frost and snaw on ilka[1] hill;
And Boreas wi' his blasts sae bauld
        Was threat'ning a' our kye[2] to kill.
Then Bell, my wife, who lo'es na strife,
        She said to me right hastily,
'Get up, gudeman, save crummie's[3] life,
        And tak' your auld cloak about ye.

'My crummie is a usefu' cow,
        An' she has come o' a gude kin',
Aft has she wet the bairns' mou',
        And I am laith that she should tyne.[4]
Get up, gudeman, it is fu' time,
        The sun shines in the lift[5] sae hie;[6]
Sloth never made a gracious end,
        Gae tak' your auld cloak about ye.'

'My cloak was ance a gude grey cloak,
        When it was fitting for my wear;
But now 'tis scantly worth a groat,
        For I ha'e worn't this thretty[7] year.
Let's spend the gear[8] that we ha'e won,
        We little ken the day we'll dee;
Then I'll be proud, sin' I ha'e sworn
        To ha'e a new cloak about me.'

'In days when our King Robert rang,[9]
        His trews[10] they cost but half-a-croun;
He said they were a groat ower dear,
        And ca'd the tailor thief and loon.[11]

He was the king that wore the croun,
        And thou'rt a man of laich[12] degree;
'Tis pride puts a' the country doun,
        Sae tak' thy auld cloak about thee.'

'Every land has its ain laugh,
        Ilk kind o' corn it has its hool;[13]
I think the warld is a' run wrang,
        When ilka wife her man wad rule.
Do ye no see Rob, Jock, and Hab,
        How they are girded[14] gallantlie;
While I sit hurklin'[15] i' the ase?[16]
        I'll ha'e a new cloak about me!'

'Gudeman, I wat 'tis thretty year
        Sin' we did ane anither ken;[17]
An' we ha'e had atween us twa
        Of lads and bonnie lasses ten;
Now they are women grown and men,
        I wish and pray well may they be;
And if you prove a good husband,
        E'en tak' your auld cloak about ye.'

Bell, my wife, she lo'es na strife,
        But she would guide me if she can;
And to maintain an easy life,
        I aft maun yield, though I'm gudeman.
Nocht's to be won at woman's han',
        Unless to gie her a' the plea;
Then I'll leave aff where I began,
        And tak' my auld cloak about me.

Anonymous

1 each	5 sky	9 reigned	12 low	15 crouching
2 cattle	6 so high	10 trousers	13 husk	16 ashes
3 pet cow	7 thirty	11 knave	14 dressed	17 know
4 be taken	8 money			

Flower of the World

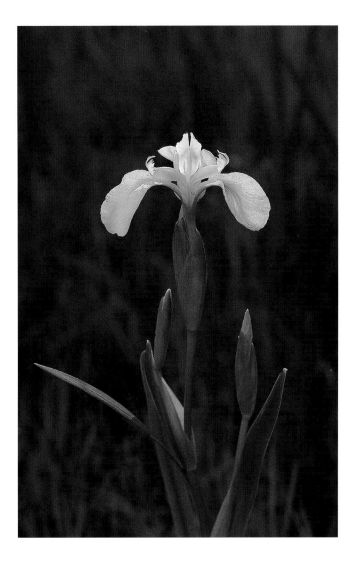

Wherever men sinned and wept,
I wandered in my quest;
At last in a Garden of God
I saw the Flower of the World.

This Flower had human eyes,
Its breath was the breath of the mouth;
Sunlight and starlight came,
And the Flower drank bliss from both.

Whatever was base and unclean,
Whatever was sad and strange,
Was piled around its roots;
It drew its strength from the same.

Whatever was formless and base
Pass'd into fineness and form;
Whatever was lifeless and mean
Grew into beautiful bloom.

Then I thought 'O Flower of the World,
Miraculous Blossom of things,
Light as a faint wreath of snow
Thou tremblest to fall in the wind:

'O beautiful Flower of the World,
Fall not nor wither away;
He is coming - He cannot be far -
The Lord of the Flow'rs and the Stars.'

And I cried 'O Spirit divine!
That walkest the Garden unseen,
Come hither, and bless, ere it dies,
The beautiful Flower of the World.'

Robert Buchanan
Born 1841

Culloden Moor
(Seen in Autumn Rain)

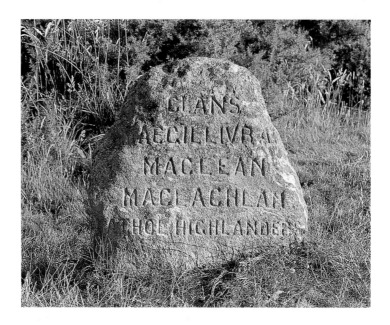

Full of grief, the low winds sweep
    O'er the sorrow-haunted ground;
Dark the woods where night rains weep,
    Dark the hills that watch around.

Tell me, can the joys of spring
    Ever make this sadness flee,
Make the woods with music ring,
    And the streamlet laugh for glee?

When the summer moor is lit
    With the pale fire of the broom,
And through green the shadows flit,
    Still shall mirth give place to gloom?

Sad shall it be, though sun be shed
    Golden bright on field and flood;
E'en the heather's crimson red
    Holds the memory of blood.

Here that broken, weary band
    Met the ruthless foe's array,
Where those moss-grown boulders stand,
    On that dark and fatal day.

Like a phantom hope had fled,
    Love to death was all in vain,
Vain, though heroes' blood was shed,
    And though hearts were broke in twain.

Many a voice has cursed the name
    Time has into darkness thrust,
Cruelty his only fame
    In forgetfulness and dust,

Noble dead that sleep below,
    We your valour ne'er forget;
Soft the heroes' rest who know
    Hearts like theirs are beating yet.

Alice Macdonell
19th Century

Gin I was God

Gin I was God, sittin' up there abeen,[1]
Weariet nae doot noo a' my darg[2] was deen,[3]
Deaved[4] wie' the harps an' hymns oonendin' ringing,
Tired o' the flockin' angels hairse[5] wi' singin',
To some clood-edge I'd daunder[6] furth an', feth,
Look ower an' watch hoo things were gyaun[7] aneth.[8]
Syne,[9] gin[10] I saw hoo men I'd made mysel'
Had startit in to pooshan,[11] sheet[12] an' fell,
To reive[13] an' rape, an' fairly mak' a hell
O' my braw birlin' Earth, - a hale week's wark -
I'd cast my coat again, rowe up my sark,[14]
An', or they'd time to lench[15] a second ark,
Tak' bak my word an' sen' anither spate,
Droon oot the hale hypothec,[16] dicht[17] the sklate,[18]
Own my mistak', an' aince I'd cleared the brod,[19]
Start a' thing ower[20] again, gin I was God.

Charles Murray
1864-1941

1 above	11 poison
2 work	12 shoot
3 done	13 harry
4 deafened	14 shirtsleeves
5 hoarse	15 launch
6 wander	16 thing
7 going	17 wipe
8 beneath	18 slate
9 then	19 board
10 if, given	20 over

LIST OF PHOTOGRAPHS